FATHER CHRISTMAS

Other books
by Raymond Briggs

FATHER CHRISTMAS GOES ON HOLIDAY
JIM AND THE BEANSTALK
FUNGUS THE BOGEYMAN
THE SNOWMAN

Based on Raymond Briggs' original story

THE SNOWMAN AND THE SNOWDOG BOOK AND CD

Raymond Briggs

Father Christmas

PUFFIN

For my Mother and Father

PUFFIN BOOKS

UK | USA | Canada | Ireland | Australia | India | New Zealand | South Africa

Puffin Books is part of the Penguin Random House group of companies
whose addresses can be found at global.penguinrandomhouse.com.

www.penguin.co.uk www.puffin.co.uk www.ladybird.co.uk

First published by Hamish Hamilton 1973
Published by Puffin Books 1974
Published in this edition 2014
004

Printed in China
A CIP catalogue record for this book is available from the British Library

ISBN: 978-0-723-29740-6

All correspondence to:
Puffin Books, Penguin Random House Children's
80 Strand, London WC2R 0RL

Father Christmas

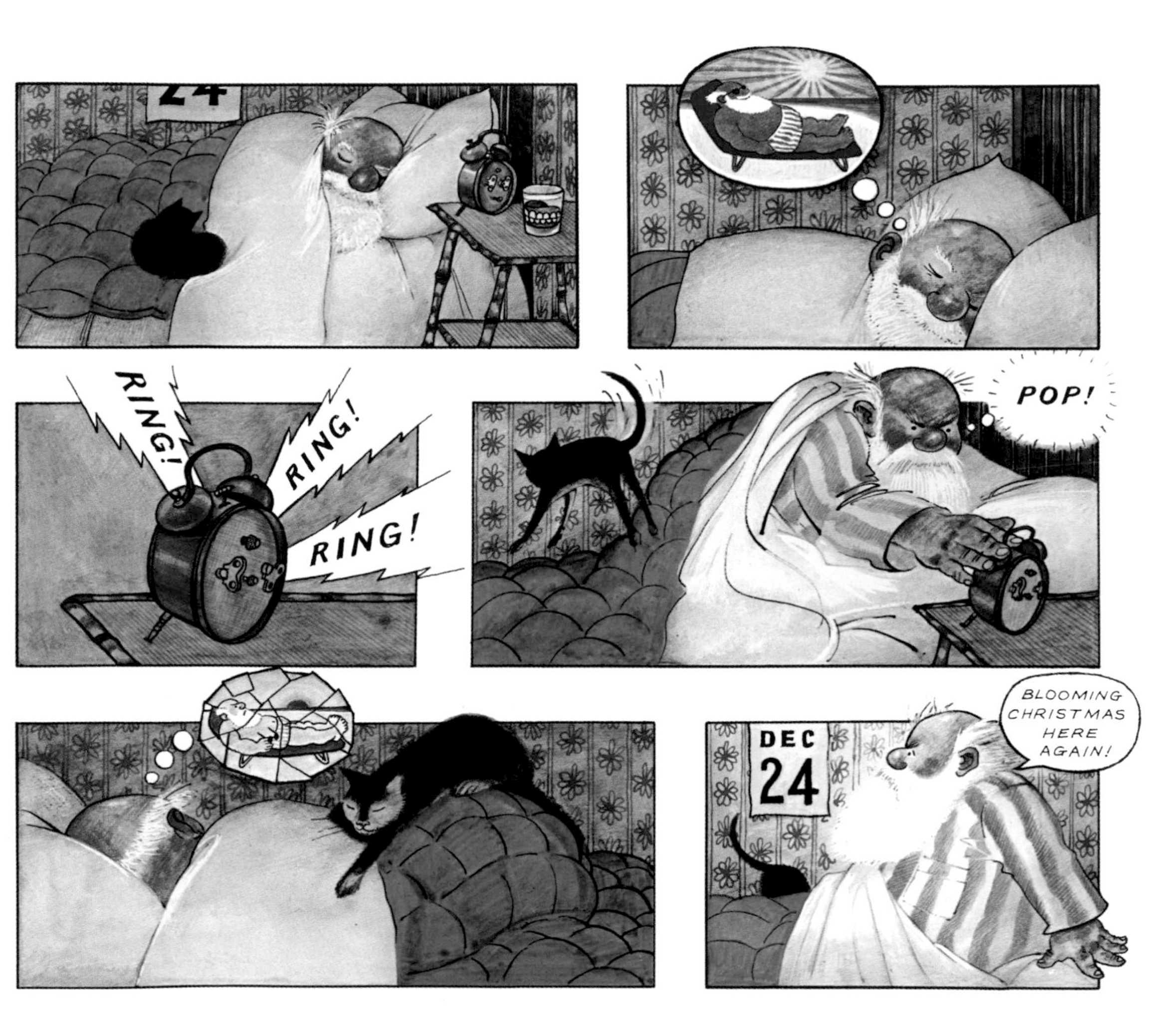

GET OFF MY SLIPPERS, DOG!

MAJORCA
BLOOMING SNOW!

YAWN

I HATE WINTER!

HERE YOU ARE, DEERS.

GOOD POT OF TEA
TEA
BLOW THE BLOOMING SNOW!
THE FROZEN NORTH WILL BE VERY COLD-SNOW, ICE, SLEET....
BRRR!
GOOD GIRL!

CAPRI
CORN FLAKES

ROLL ON SUMMER!
ARCTIC ECHO
SNOW, SNOW AND MORE SNOW

MALTA
UXO
UXO

BRR! BLOOMING COLD!

WORK, WORK, WORK!

KEEP STILL YOU SILLY DEERS !

GOODBYE CAT
GOODBYE DOG

GIDDY UP!

TALLY-HO!

BLOOMING SNOW!

RAIN NOW! WHAT NEXT?

!!! xxx
WEATHER!

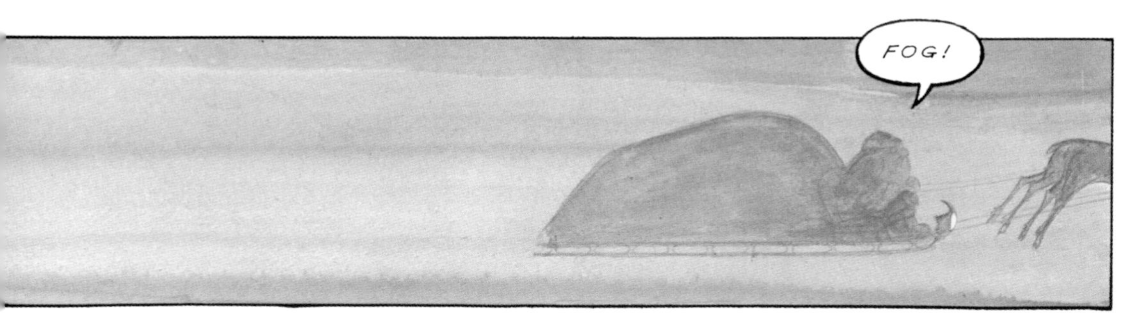
FOG!

BLOOMING CHIMNEYS!

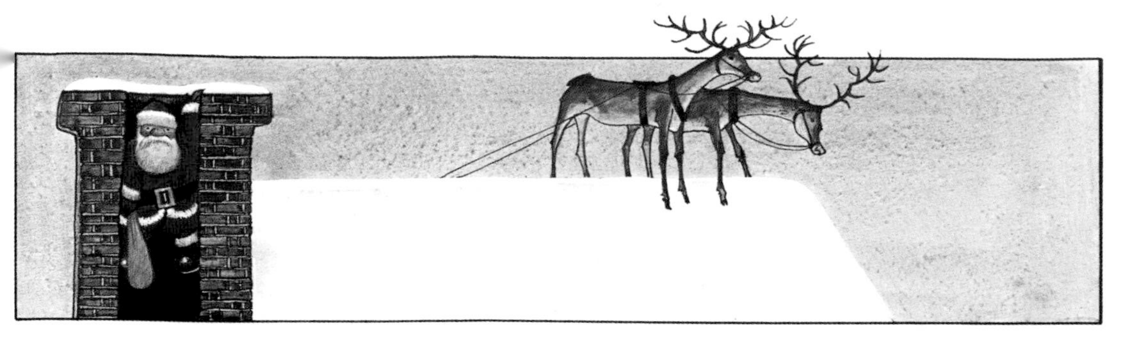

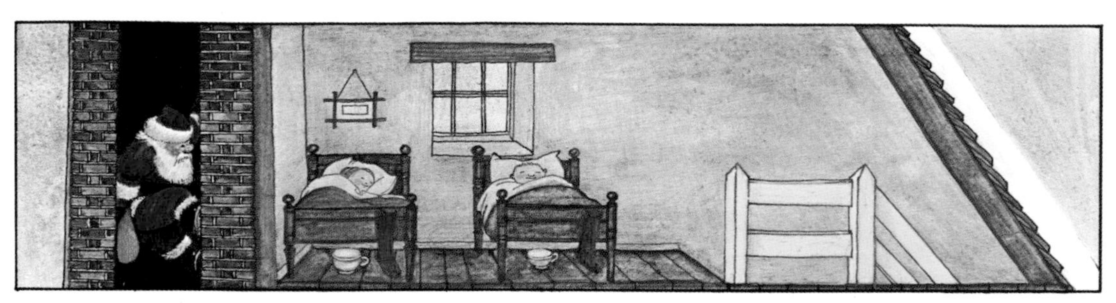

BLOOMING SOOT!
8 THIS WAY PLEAS

BRIGHTON
LANE
UNDERHILL
DITCHLING
CATTLE

HM, BETTER THAN NOTHING I SUPPOSE.
FOR FATHER CHRISTMAS

WHOA!

65

TEA
TEA

GRRR!
SNOW, ICE, FROST, SLEET, HAIL, RAIN

BLOOMING AERIALS!
FOR FATHER christmas
BLOOMING CATS!

BETTER GET A MOVE ON!

HM, NO BLOOMING CHIMNEYS, ANYWAY.

DAFT PLACE TO LIVE!

BLOOMING COOKERS!
STAIRS, STAIRS, STAIRS.
DEAR SANTA DAD SAYS HELP YOURSELF
LOVELY!
HOW DO I GET INTO THIS THING?
AAACHOO!
GETTING A BLOOMING COLD, NOW.
STILL AT IT, MATE?
NEARLY DONE.
MILK
ERB 190D
ONLY ONE MORE, NOW.

GOOD! THE FLAG'S FLYING. THEY'RE IN.

WHOA!
HOORAY! HOME AGAIN.

BRR! BLOOMING FEET FROZEN!

HULLO, CAT! HULLO, DOG!

NICE CLEAN STRAW, DEERS.

GOOD CUP OF TEA.

HARK THE HERALD ANGELS SING

LOVELY PUD!

HM! PRESENTS! SEEN ENOUGH OF THOSE THINGS FOR ONE DAY.

NOTHING LIKE A GOOD BATH.

HARK THE HERALD ANGELS SING

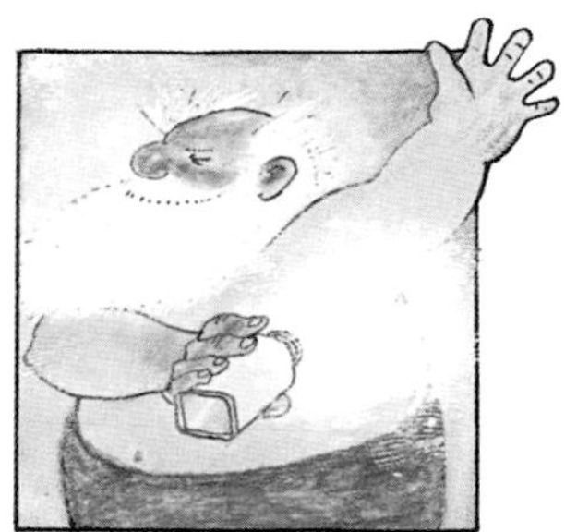

NICE CLEAN SOCKS

GOOD DROP OF ALE.

TWA

LOVELY GRUB!
VIN RED PARTY SIZE

BLOOMING AWFUL TIE FROM AUNTY ELSIE!

HORRIBLE SOCKS FROM COUSIN VIOLET!

AH! THAT'S MORE LIKE IT. GOOD OLD FRED!
V.S.O.P.
COGNAC
10 STAR

TEA

FIDDLING BUTTONS!
24
25
24
THAT'S THAT DONE FOR ANOTHER YEAR.
HAPPY CHRISTMAS CAT!
HAPPY CHRISTMAS DOG!
HAPPY BLOOMING CHRISTMAS TO YOU, TOO!

The End